To My Child You Are Loved

Written by C.M.P Smith

Illustrated by Olivia Chevallier

You are a **BIG** shining *Treasure* wrapped up in a bow,

full of *Wonder* and EXCITEMENT.

...The best gift you can bestow.

So I really want you to know...

When you came into being, my child,
I knew you were...

...Special,

Loved,

Adored.

I want you to know, my child,
to feel it in your **heart**, in your **SOUL**,
that **YOU ARE LOVED.**

You are loved.

Not for who you were yesterday,
or who you will be tomorrow.

Know that right here, right now, you are **PERFECT**,

you are *Special*.

You are exactly who you are meant to be.

As I embrace you in a **Cuddle MONSTER** my child, I want you to know you *deserve* and will always deserve to be...

...embraced within my arms... ...and within my **love.**

This is **your moment**;
Know it and embrace it.
Connect with my love.
Connect with the love for
yourself.

connect...

...with the people around you

Connect with the earth that nourishes you...

Connect with God, nature and creation.

Whatever that is or is not.

Feel the wonderful, magical moment we are in right now.

Beat your drum and beat it LOUD at YOUR OWN PERFECT RHYTHM...

Whether you can stand upon your head...

...you're good at maths...

$(x-4)(x+3)$
$= x^2 + 3x - 4x - 12$
$= x^2$

...or arts...

...it matters not,

As long as you know in your **heart**, in your **soul**, you can **grow** and **learn**, and that you are LOVED.

In this moment, right here, right now, if this day is filled with **joy, wonder, ecstasy.** I want you to know this day is yours and that you should fully and wholly feel it and embrace it. Without any shame or guilt. You deserve this day.

This is your perfect day.

But, if this moment
is filled with

ANGER,

SADNESS,

or

Heart⚡ache,

know, my child,
this is just a moment,
your emotions are here to help you.
Listen to them, **kindly** sit with them
and let them **pass on by** like a

Thunderstorm.

When you feel stuck in a blue-greyish day and your smile is stuck upside down,

Know my child, you are still perfect to me, even with your frown.

Remember to prioritise rest, recharge, snuggle and take time to heal.
Know, my child, in your heart, in your soul that you will rise up and
feel at peace again.

... and the seasons. Forever changing and evolving. Just like you, my child.

Notice and admire the ... budding of the flower...

...Find yourself habitually smiling

Let whole-hearted **Joy**

as you wander into the warmth of the sun.

welcome the snow...

Sometimes...

I will get it wrong,

...because I am **HUMAN** and **growing** and perfectly imperfect,

just like you, my child.

So...

I will be a **COURAGEOUS** leader, and show you how to make repairs, because our mistakes do not define us, they simply help us *Learn* and *grow*.

Know my child,
Perfection is not
something to be sought,
that you are already

Good Enough

Hold *Kindness*, Compassion, LOVE and COURAGE and let *Vulnerability* and Passion be your guiding light.

I hope and pray that I will **grow old** and **grey** and always be there for you my child,

to have the honour and the grace to stand beside you, stand behind you...

...As you BOLDLY GRASP this moment with *passion,*

so I can let you know, my child,

within your **heart,** your **soul,** that you are LOVED.

You already have everything you need, you can continue to shine bright.

Share your wonder and embrace and love this life.

My child you are loved. Be proud of what makes you unique and be confident to share yourself with the world.

I know it every day when I see the *twinkle* in your eye, as you smile. As you light up the room, you are perfect right now as you are.

You are **loved completely** and **entirely** from your head, right to your toes, know, my child, you are, you were... ...and you always will be **LOVED**, and are just **PERFECT** as you are.

The End

This book is dedicated to:

. My passionate redhead, my emotionally intelligent first daughter, who came into this world and looked into my eyes and gave me a gift of growth, courage, healing and love. I hope she always embraces her uniqueness.

. My crazy deep blue-eyed second daughter, who has an amazing passion for life, with such self-assurance and peace in the world. She continues to inspire me every day to live in the present and love completely. I hope she will continue to embrace each new day with enthusiasm and excitement.

~ C.M.P Smith

The Cuddle Monster game

This is a fun game with lots of laughs and giggles. A great game to play with your grown-ups when you want to feel loved.

The grown up is a clumsy, floundering monster who wants to grab hold of you and cuddle you lots and never let go. You have to try and escape the monster and you always manage to escape. But.. the monster comes back for more cuddles and sometimes kisses too.

Can you draw a big cuddle monster, what would it look like?

I love you.. rhyming game

In this game you take it in turns to declare how much you love each other and the other person replies with something else that rhymes. We love to play it at the dinner table, while out walking or when we're in the car.

"I love you more than the moon and the stars...
        "I love you more than my shiny toy cars"

"I love you more than a juicy ripe peach..
        "I love you more than playing at the beach"

What rhymes will you come up with together?